Leonard Barras has had two books previously published by Iron Press, *Hailstones On Your Father*, a collection of preposterous verses, and a volume of his hilariously sad prose pieces, *Bluebottles On My Marmalade*. His oeuvre also includes the stage plays *A Little Stiff-Built Chap* and *The Shy Gasman* (both premiered by Alan Ayckbourn at Scarborough), *Cushy Butterfield*, *The Night of the Snapped Suspender* and *Tight at the Back*, which was produced this year at Newcastle Playhouse. He first came to notice in 1949, writing a weekly newspaper column (*Through My Hat*) and a weekly radio script – for the legendary *Wot Cheor, Geordie* programme. He has continued to write for the press and for radio (he was associated with the award-winning *Northern Drift*), as well as writing the BBC 2 comedy series *Mother Nature's Bloomer's*, starring Roy Kinnear.

The various pieces collected in this volume were broadcast on Radio 4 between 1982 and 1986.

Also by Leonard Barras

HAILSTONES ON YOUR FATHER
BLUEBOTTLES ON MY MARMALADE

UP THE TYNE IN A FLUMMOX

Leonard Barras
With illustrations by
Geoff Laws

Futura
IRON

A Futura/Iron Book

First published in Great Britain in 1987 by
Futura Publications, a Division of Macdonald
& Co (Publishers) Ltd
London & Sydney
in association with
IRON Press
Tyne & Wear
IRON Press gratefully acknowledges
the financial assistance of Northern Arts.

ISBN 0 7088 3571 6

Printed and bound in Great Britain by
The Guernsey Press

IRON Press
5 Marden Terrace, Cullercoats
North Shields, Tyne & Wear NE30 4PD

Futura Publications
A Division of Macdonald & Co (Publishers)
Ltd
Greater London House
Hampstead Road
London NW1 7QX

A BPCC plc Company

CONTENTS

A Fearful Conflagration

The Rope Works fire, my Uncle Hal always said, was like Shaw's description of a General Election in a capitalist society. I was nine years old at the time, it was one o'clock in the morning and I was sleeping fitfully with my head at the bottom of the bed because of toothache when my old Aunt Emma burst in.

'Throw on your vest!' she shouted. 'The Rope Works is on fire!'

'Where is it?' I asked.

'At the bottom of Stony Bank, you should know that,' she cried.

'I was thinking of my vest,' I said.

'I should hope so,' she said. She had brought me up always to think of my vest. 'But where are your glasses?'

'Where are my cigarette cards?' I responded.

'What's wrong with the lad?' Uncle Hal called from the kitchen, where he was throwing on his bowler hat, because it was Sunday.

'It's just that he's never seen me in my nightie before,'

said my old Aunt Emma, throwing on her mackintosh.

The Rope Works! Many a time I had got my elbow jammed in its railings. And now, as we stepped out of the door, it seemed that everybody was hurtling down Stony Bank to see the blaze, the toothache epidemic that had been sweeping Wallsend forgotten.

'This stampede,' Uncle Hal panted, 'is like Shaw's description of a General Election in a capitalist society.'

'This is when you need a bicycle, you see,' my old Aunt Emma reproached him. Uncle Hal had lost his bicycle during the heavy rains of 1930.

'The Fire Brigade!' Uncle Hal shouted. 'What about the Fire Brigade?'

'They've got an engine, Uncle Hal,' I said.

But Uncle Hal had made a detour to the door of P.C. Jack Townsend. Consumed as always with public-spiritedness, he had decided that he must urge the policeman to cycle off to the Fire Station to entreat them to come.

P.C. Townsend said he would have done it, nobody sooner. 'But it's my leg,' he explained.

He was a diffident man, reluctant to get involved in unseemly matters, and would sit in his lodgings in dressing gown and pyjamas rather than apprehend murderers. Notified by his landlady that the Rope Works was ablaze, he had made a token gesture of putting on his uniform, but had missed his trouser leg and fallen quite heavily on his knee.

'Its's a nasty night for a fire,' said my old Aunt Emma.

'Would you like a cup of tea?' asked P.C. Townsend's landlady.

'I'll let the doctor see my knee,' said P.C. Townsend.

But Uncle Hal was already binding on the policeman's bicycle clips. When he arrived at the Fire Station, the man at the door said they were all out at the fire. 'I've stayed

behind because of toothache,' he confided.

'You must understand,' said Uncle Hal, 'that this bicycle doesn't fit me.' It was a perfectly good machine, but he had always resented that the policeman, as society's lackey, was provided with a free bicycle.

'They're at the Rope Works,' said the man. 'Turn left at Stony Bank.'

'By such bribery, you see,' said Uncle Hal, 'does capitalism ensure its survival.'

'If you see the chief,' said the man, 'will you give him this?'

'Pardon?' said Uncle Hal,

'It's just that he took the wrong helmet,' said the man.

My old Aunt Emma and I had meanwhile drunk our tea and proceeded to the Rope Works. 'See those flames licking up to the sky,' she said.

'I haven't got my glasses,' I said. They were with my cigarette cards in the gas meter cupboard.

Uncle Hal arrived and accosted the Fire Chief. 'Can you not see the lad's got his elbow in the railings?' he said.

'Get your foot out of my bucket!' the Fire Chief shouted.

'Its *your* foot that's in the bucket!' Uncle Hal shouted back.

'Can I help it,' said the Fire Chief, 'if I've got the wrong helmet?'

The fire lasted five hours and they had to pump the Gut dry to put it out, finding Uncle Hal's bicycle.

Next day, I went down with my stomach, in the gas meter cupboard. 'It serves him right for going out in nothing but a vest,' Dr. Duncan said. He sounded my elbow and my stomach and prescribed syrup of figs and embrocation. 'Not that he'll survive,' he added, speaking sourly because of toothache.

'Embrocation and syrup of figs?' said my old Aunt Emma. 'What if we get them mixed up?'

'That'll save time,' Dr. Duncan acknowledged.

'You should sleep upside down for toothache,' my old Aunt Emma recommended. She had acquired a lot of cures from Granny Tate, who had buried three husbands.

Dr. Duncan warned her against letting me make a habit of running down Stony Bank at one o'clock on a cold morning.

'There was a fire at the Rope Works,' said my old Aunt Emma.

'You can't always count on that,' he said sternly.

'How's Jack?' said my old Aunt Emma.

'Who?' said Dr. Duncan.

'The policeman,' said my old Aunt Emma. 'You should put him in a cold bath with Epsom salts.'

Dr. Duncan thanked her and said he had his own ways of losing patients.

Herbert Mangle, the Wallsend poet, felt constrained to celebrate the occasion in rhyme, but his lyric, though vivid, was necessarily vicarious, as he had unaccountably got locked in the off-licence with Mrs Proudfoot, the proprietress:

O fearful conflagration!
O awesome dazzling sight!
The Rope Works flames emblazoned
The Wallsend sky that night:
A scene that quite eluded
This prisoner of lust -
Still clasped long after daybreak
To Mrs Proudfoot's bust.

Uncle Hal said the fire had been like Shaw's description of a General Election in a capitalist society.

'You keep saying that,' said my old Aunt Emma.

'In Shaw's allegory, mind you,' said Uncle Hal, 'it was a runaway cow they were pursuing.'

'There's a lot of this toothache about,' said my old Aunt Emma. "Still, you got your bicycle back, apart from the wheels."

'They were enslaved by the capitalist system, you see!' cried Uncle Hal,

'He freed the bairn's elbow,' said my old Aunt Emma, 'in spite of his bucket.'

Three weeks later, Uncle Hal burst in on me as I slept fitfully on my stomach. 'It's the General Election!' he shouted. 'The result's declared!'

I threw on my glasses to dash out to follow the cow, but he only wanted to tell me that the capitalists had survived again. On the whole, I would have preferred a fire.

Not the Food of Love

Sitting on a coalhouse the other night, I was reminded that when I was in love with Juanita St. Fortinbras, we both wore glasses, and for all I know still do. I know mine still keep dropping off.

Juanita St. Fortinbras! The daughter of an eccentric self-made design and outfit draughtsman with a fierce moustache, she went out of my life in the days of chocolate rationing, whispering, 'Don't look when I go,' not that I could, because my glasses had dropped off.

Kissing a girl when you're a bashful lad and you both wear glasses is not easy, especially when you have displaced biceps from badminton. 'Juanita ...' I would breathe.

'Mind my glasses,' she would say.

Constant clashes of glasses wounded her sensibilities and a time came when, passionate after the badminton club, we tangled lenses yet again and my steel frames caught in her hair while her horn rims went up my nose. It seemed better to part. 'Goodbye, then,' I breathed. I breathed a lot in those days. She went home to her keyboard.

She and her five sisters, nurtured in luxury, had been taught music and knitting from an early age and frequently sat up until eleven o'clock, playing Brahms and Debussy on various parts of the piano, wherever they could fit in, while their father cursed on the hearthrug. She was an untamed girl, being her father's daughter, as they all were, and I felt she needed my steadying influence, because there was already one leg off the piano.

I was sitting on her coalhouse one night during that aching wilderness of 1947.

'Wait there,' she had whispered. 'I shall call you in when daddy goes to bed.'

Her father, himself an obsessive accompanist, had advanced from his rug, dismissed the other girls to their rooms to knit, in their winceyette nighties, and was spending the evening leading Juanita in rather abandoned songs at the piano. 'One more chorus of Beethoven's Pastoral!' I heard him shouting. 'One more chorus of Mendelssohn's B Minor Quartet! If you don't know the words, my dear, la-la!'

At half-past eleven, Juanita said, 'Daddy, the fire is getting low. Shall I fill the scuttle?'

'Better not go out there, my love,' he said. 'There's a man on the coalhouse.'

My biceps had turned blue by then, but by way of compensation I kept getting glimpses at certain upstairs windows of winceyette nighties. It was midnight when her father took a wrong turning on a Liszt symphonic poem, jammed his moustache in the music stand and had to retire with an eccentric curse. Juanita hurried out, but I had gone home to my cocoa, because even for a bashful lad winceyette nighties can begin to pall.

I suppose I might have joined in the musical evenings, even if it meant filling the coal scuttle, but the only tune I knew in those days was Jerome Kern's *What Depth is the Sea*? which I've since learned was by Irving Berlin and entitled *How Deep is the Ocean*? Knitting I could have managed, because my old Aunt Emma had brought me up in the precept that every lad should be able to darn his socks and make cocoa in the event of the Apocalypse, rather than go to Armageddon barefoot on any empty stomach, and I had in fact knitted half a pair of mitts at the time when Juanita and I lost our last badminton match together.

'Please get your steel frames out of my hair,' she said, and when we had gone our separate ways, she to Brahms and I to my left mitt, I reflected that Rupert Brooke was right and it's as well to find a girl with glasses as wise but kindlier and susceptibilities as soft but true.

Mind you, she tried to teach me, on those rare occasions when her father went to bed, how to spell Liszt, without success. I almost conquered Donizetti one rapturous evening, but fell over the hearthrug when my glasses dropped off.

I loved a few girls after that in a few more aching wildernesses, but never another badminton player. As Herbert Mangle, the Wallsend poet, wrote of his own rueful affair with the greengrocer's niece:

When my feet are hurting and my head is bad
    And my torso's badly dented,
I think of all those times we had:
    Yes, I remember you,
    Hilda Mulgrew,
        As I hug my first-aid kit.

It isn't just my chest and knee.

I've also got this broken heart,
For that is what you did to me.
Oh, I can't blame you
For my bout of 'flu,
But that apart, but that apart . . .

When you've got your backache and the human race
Seems acutely represented
By my remembered ugly face,
Recall you loved me too,
Hilda Mulgrew,
For a fortnight and a bit.

Nor did I ever love another girl with glasses. For me, a girl with glasses will always mean that wild badminton player I last breathed on in January, 1948. Of course, Rachel Hocking came along to help me over it, and Diana Green and Nora Trannock, but they were respectively a tap dancer, a bell-ringer and a graphologist. I tried to ring bells with Diana Green, but she never understood why I brought my badminton racquet.

Not that I've let my falling glasses stand in the way of a fulfilled life. Apart from ringing bells, I've been secretary of the Homing Pigeons' Old Boys' Association, run after buses, walked the Pennine Way for nearly a mile-and-a-half, knitted another mitt and even learned to spell Bela Bartók.

When I last heard of Juanita St. Fortinbras, she had sunk further into Brahms and Debussy and without my steadying influence had even lapsed into Schumann. Her sisters had gone, eschewing winceyette and claiming their share of the piano legs. As for her father, he's long dead, and if it's true that Beethoven can hear in heaven, he'll not be very pleased with what a design and outfit draughtsman can do to the Pastoral.

Why, after untold years, do I find myself sitting on coalhouses? Well, memories refuse to die and it's still painful when I sing *How Deep is the Ocean*?, so people tell me. Some things you can't forget when you've got recurring displaced biceps. On the whole, the wound has healed, but she's got my chocolate ration.

Nothing Like Flute Practise

'Well, if you ask me . . . ' is a preface used by people like Albert Fairhurst who are seldom asked anything, because they are going to tell you anyway.

Albert Fairhurst was a jobbing printer who was always right. His wife Norma, who longed for a life beyond the front door, where she had heard there was unbridled hedonism, had never wholly loved him, or jobbing printing, but she was one of eight sisters and had married him with a headache. For quite some time, she took his assertions for honest forthrightness, and was rather fond of his ginger hair, but after ten years she realised that she was finishing fewer sentences than she had even at home. It was twelve-and-a-half years, be it said, before forbearance expired.

Their budgie was at first a joy to her and she taught it to recite the works of William Blake, backwards. Before long, however, Fairhurst was interrupting it when it was halfway through 'Wild southern the in me bore mother my,' with shouts of, 'Well, if you ask me . . . ' and it developed a psychological blockage and retreated into the corner of its cage, hiding under its wing.

To do him justice, and we should always do justice to an opinionated jobbing printer, Fairhurst was a victim of the consumer society. For all his truculence, he was suggestible. He felt persecuted. He vacillated. He was a fair representative of the human race.

As a symbolic consumer, he was obsessively convinced that greengrocers and glass bevellers and scaffolding hirers were linked in a conspiracy to defraud him. 'I wouldn't except even water treatment chemists,' he had remarked those many years earlier to young Norma Mooney, as she then was.

'I've always found water treatment chemists an honourable band of men,' young Norma had responded, and having thus taken him aback, she said, 'Please sit down again,' and asked him to elope with her.

'What was that?' he said, because her seven sisters were in the room at the time.

She repeated the question and he vacillated for three days, but his suggestibility won in the end and he married her in order to feel persecuted.

He settled down with his bride, suspiciously, in a little home built by O.J. Woodburn and Sons, contractors. He was far from happy about its construction, having heard that O.J. Woodburn laid his foundations on decayed vegetable matter, and he feared that the whole house might blow away one day while he was in the Red Lion. 'Mark my words, that decayed vegetable matter will come home to roost,' he told Norma. By that time, he was not merely persecuted; he was also mixing metaphors.

'And I'll tell you something,' he pronounced one day, staring into the cage. 'We should never have got a green budgie.'

'So you've said,' Norma sighed, shifting some bevelled glass, 'but it's a blue budgie.' It was on their honeymoon that she had tried to tell him that he was colour-blind, but he was vacillating uncontrollably at the time and the chance was missed.

'Is soul my O!' the budgie said, staring back, 'but black am I . . . '

'The thing is,' shouted Fairhurst, 'we're stuck with a green budgie, let's face it, I mean to say!' Eventually, the budgie stopped talking except to itself.

It was after twelve years that Norma took to writing letters, in the hope of attracting life to her front door. Her seven sisters were by then scattered to various corners of the earth and were married with nineteen children, so it wasn't long before she was getting sacksful of replies from them, offering exotic remedies for her headache, now returned with increased virulence.

'Well, well, Mrs Norma Fairhurst,' the postman said one morning. 'A parcel today from Hong Kong, plus the usual six letters.'

'It's my head,' Norma volunteered. 'Would you like a cup of cocoa?'

'I've got relations in Southport,' said the postman, 'but with me it's my back.' He told Norma that he often thought about the purpose of life and would have thought about it more if he hadn't had backache. 'Is there a Supreme Being concurrent with the universe?' he asked.

'Only a jobbing printer, as far as I know,' said Norma.

'And has He given me intelligence,' the postman said, 'so that I can ponder the purpose of life?'

'Have a Jaffa cake,' Norma offered.

'And if so, couldn't I ponder it better,' the postman pursued, 'if He hadn't burdened me with lumbago?' He sometimes put it to people, he said, that humanity was consistently aberrant, but they tended not to answer him.

'We don't go on making the same mistakes,' Norma suggested, 'only similar ones,' an indication that if it hadn't been for her seven sisters, her headache and her husband, she might have carved out a career as a calendar motto writer, an enterprise in which her father had tried to encourage her before he had forgotten which one she was.

'Keep up the flute practice, Ethel,' he had said.

'I'm Norma, father,' she had responded.

'Nothing like flute practice in moderation,' he had counselled. 'Or table tennis.'

'It's calendar motto writing, father,' she had murmured.

'All right, Alice!' he had said.

There came a night when Albert Fairhurst burst in with the news that water treatment chemists had penetrated the Black Lion. 'The thing is,' he accused, 'they're contaminating the lager. Where's the string?'

'What string?' said Norma. 'It's the Red Lion.'

But he was searching for brown wrapping paper. The Black Lion, he said, was no longer a fit place for a civilised jobbing printer. Thereafter, he took to spending his evenings at home, exercising his suggestibility and parcelling up sets of faulty belt dressings to take back to Messrs McPhillips and Theaker's department store.

McPhillips and Theaker had been persecuting him for a long time and he had had occasion to take back to them such items as a corroded hessian stenciller, an imperfect sausage skin and a leaky grass drier.

'This belt dressing's faulty,' he would say to Norma, throwing string about.

'Have you a message for Alice or Christine or Ethel?' she would ask, 'before I seal the . . .'

'If you ask me,' he would say, 'there's no grey wrapping paper.'

'Rage a in heaven all puts,' the budgie would mutter to itself, 'cage a in redbreast robin . . . '

'Another thing,' Fairhurst would shout, 'I'm taking this hessian stenciller back tomorrow.'

Like all bigots, he believed himself a model of tolerance, but so far from offering him any satisfaction, McPhillips and Theaker had hardened their attitude into one of blatant animosity, which had culminated in a nasty incident in Gents' Outfitting, when McPhillips had struck him fiercely with a frayed cummerbund. Presently they took to getting under the counter when they saw him coming.

It was some time before he became aware of Norma's preoccupation with correspondence, because he hurried out of the house every morning before the post arrived, so that he could spend as much time as possible at the jobbing printers', contradicting the devils.

'Mind you,' the postman said to Norma one day, 'I can't see all these exotic remedies doing much for the budgie's head.'

'Wisdom of palace the to leads excess of road the,' the budgie said.

'I never looked at it like that,' the postman said, sitting down to his cocoa.

The budgie had by now retreated into glum self-sufficiency. It had reasoned that Fairhurst, William Blake, Norma and the postman were equally to blame for its psychological blockage. In a happier story than this, it would be flying freely in its native Australia, but we need it for the dénouement.

'It's talking to itself,' Norma explained, 'because it's not the wrong colour.'

She was hoping the postman would speak of the world

beyond her front door, but he was enquiring again if humanity was uniformly erratic.

'I speak for the rotting hulk that is me,' he said. 'Am I inadequate, frightened, argumentative?'

'It is I who have the head,' Norma reminded him. 'But better sympathy misplaced than well-aimed malice,' she added, evoking her mislaid vocation.

The postman hadn't looked at it like that either. 'I was reading in the Amateur Dermatologist,' he said, 'that three-fifths of the rubbish that goes into our vacuum cleaners has flaked off the human body.'

Norma accepted thirteen letters and opened a packet of chocolate fingers. Global correspondence, it seemed, would have to serve as an unsatisfactory substitute for calendar motto writing. Of course, Ethel's flute practice had hardly prospered even before her marriage, but at least their father had not called her Alice.

'I see the point,' she said, 'about your rubbishy hulk.' Was she taking the postman's introspections for acute discernment? 'My father,' she went on, 'used to advise a moderate amount of table tennis, admittedly to the wrong daughter, and I feel . . . '

'What's more,' said the postman, 'am I inept and guilt-ridden?'

Norma passed him the chocolate fingers, not noticing that she had failed to finish a sentence.

One night, when Norma was watching *Coronation Street* and Fairhurst was telling her with supreme certainty what would happen in the next eleven episodes, he paused, flung aside his frayed cummerbund and said, 'I'll tell you something.'

Twelve-and-a-half years had gone; forbearance was ebbing fast. 'As a matter of fact,' Norma said, 'I was going to say . . . '

'If you ask me,' Fairhurst interrupted, 'it's time you stopped this tomfoolery of forever writing letters, let's face it.'

Norma gazed with residual fondness at his ginger hair. 'Oddly enough,' she murmured, 'you may be . . . '

'Right?' said Fairhurst. 'Of course I'm right, I mean to say!' And he told her it would snow next morning, whatever her new barometer said.

Next morning, however, he awoke to the realisation that if he did not shake off his sense of persecution he was doomed to a life of mixed metaphors or worse. It was Norma's birthday and he hurried downstairs to unveil the barometer he had bought for her. She hadn't wanted a barometer, because she already had a centrifugal pump and a theodolite, which she didn't want either. Halcyon day though it was, the barometer registered: 'Hurricane'. Angrily, Fairhurst snatched it up and hurried out of the house.

'Today's my day for ineptitude,' the postman told Norma. He couldn't even get his vacuum cleaner to work, he said; the bits that had flaked off him would just have to lie.

'Butter is mad twice a year,' said Norma, falling back, as we all do, on plagiarism. 'How do you feel about unbridled hedonism?'

'Pardon?' said the postman.

'For your bad back,' Norma suggested. It was recommended by experts and the tabloid press, she said, as the universal panacea.

The postman said he hadn't seen it advertised on television, but on reflection decided that he seldom saw anything else advertised on television. 'Are these the same experts,' he asked uneasily, 'who in my youth were saying it would lead to knee rot and the collapse of Western civilisation?' He rose from his seat.

'I keep dreaming,' said Norma, 'of life beyond my front door.'

'I don't think I'll bother with a Jaffa cake,' said the postman, vacillating palpably.

'Please sit down again,' said Norma.

When Fairhurst rushed into the store, McPhillips and Theaker came out from under the counter. It was a lovely day, they agreed, and they would certainly replace the barometer. Would he also accept a free sludge activator, with their compliments to his wife?

At these words, Fairhurst felt the persecution lifting from him, and into its place swept a euphoria mixed with a not unpleasant sense of suggestibility that urged him to call at the Red Lion. The manager there greeted him with the assurance that his strictures had been heeded; he would find the lager free from any taint of water treatment chemistry.

So Albert Fairhurst went home, a happy consumer at last. As he turned into the street, he was calling out, 'Are you there, Norma?' He was going to tell her that he loved her, even though she thought his brown hair was ginger.

Norma was not there. It was the budgie's voice that he heard. Norma had gone, to make not necessarily the same mistake, but a similar one. 'I was in a printing house in hell,' said the budgie, the right way round.

It was talking to itself in an empty space where the little house had been, for O.J. Woodburn's decayed vegetable matter had come home to roost.

A Hanging Matter

As a vegetarian republican, Uncle Hal ought not to have been present when King George the Fifth opened the new Tyne Bridge, but he was there to settle an argument with Miss Walker, the Freudian school-teacher, as to whether the king's beard was a dark shade of black. At the same time, his own burgeoning moustache, described by Miss Walker as a belated virility symbol, was under some scrutiny.

The debate began at a meeting of the Water Colour Society in the ping pong hut. Miss Walker submitted an experimental cubist vignette of the Prince Regent, on a state visit to Wallsend, circa 1811, emerging from the Dun Cow, leaning heavily on Spencer Perceval. Perceval was depicted as a parallelogram and the Prince Regent's whiskers were hexagonal. Uncle Hal claimed that not only were very few of the Hanoverians six-sided; they were also notably clean-shaven. Miss Walker retorted that the Prince Regent had a hexagonal soul, or if not, that was how she, the artist, was permitted to see him.

Jas Hunkers, family butcher and royalist, rose to aver that it was well known that the royal family was carnivorous and in consequence covered in hair. His special offer for that week, he added, was a halfpenny of tripe.

'What about Queen Mary?' Uncle Hal demanded.

'Pardon?' said Jas Hunkers.

'You see!' said Uncle Hal.

Unveiling his own water colour of a hirsute Prince Albert, Jas Hunkers said that it was undeniable that from Queen Victoria's consort had sprung a vast number of hairy descendants. He stabbed a cruel finger at Uncle Hal's bare face, shouting, 'He who can, does!'

This purloining of a Shavianism wounded Uncle Hal abominably and next day he went for a long walk along the Gut in a drizzle, agitatedly nibbling radishes, and came back with the first stirrings of a ginger moustache.

'Life levels all men,' he told my old Aunt Emma, and went into the backyard in his combinations to run on the spot in practice for the Free Thinkers' Cross-Country, for which the tripe-trained favourite was Jas Hunkers, hailed by the Wallsend Weekly Buffoon's racing correspondent as the Golden Miller of the meat emporium. In Miss Walker's view, they were both over-compensating for their departed youth and would have to come to painful terms with their Ids, or even their Egos.

By the end of the week, Uncle Hal's moustache had flourished so splendidly that it was eulogised in the Buffoon by Herbert Mangle, the Wallsend poet:

Oh, ginger tash! – set firm betwixt the nose and mouth,
  Which seems the most appropriate of places;
Earth hath not anything to show in north or south
  That's more endowed with finest hairs and graces.

It was still drizzling on the day of the cross-country, so Uncle Hal ran in a sou'wester and with his combinations back to front. Whether because of this or because life was levelling men, he was facing the wrong way at the start and stood heavily on the butcher's foot.

'I suppose you know you've broken my big toe!' Jas Hunkers shouted.

'I can't see why you're complaining,' said Uncle Hal reasonably. 'If you'd been Golden Miller, you'd have had to be shot.' And he went on to win by two-and-a-half miles from old Billy Duckwood, who at 95 was too far advanced for over-compensation.

The drizzle eased off a week later for the opening of the new Tyne Bridge, but Uncle Hal learned nothing about King George the Fifth's beard. Just as the royal party came in sight, he took cramp in his calf through running on the spot and lurched into a mounted policeman's horse.

There might have been an unpleasant scene but my old Aunt Emma calmed the policeman down with a lump of sugar. She always carried a lump of sugar in case Uncle Hal lurched into a horse.

Queen Mary was rubbing a smut off King George's nose at the time, so they both missed the incident, but an equerry detailed the Lord Mayor to send a lieutenant-colonel to see what was going on. Uncle Hal straightened himself up and said worse things happened at sea if you didn't think about it, and would the colonel thank the King for his kind interest in a lowly subject? The colonel said not at all, His Majesty was devoted to horses, and rejoined the procession, out of step, and the new Tyne Bridge was opened six minutes late.

Next day, Uncle Hal called on Miss Walker. While he had been lying under the horse with cramp, he explained, his whole life had flashed by and he had realised it was Bernard

Shaw who had black whiskers and not King George, unless they were ginger.

'By way of atonement,' he told my old Aunt Emma that night, 'I'll paint Miss Walker's portrait in the nude, from imagination.'

'I see the drizzle's stopped,' said my old Aunt Emma.

But Uncle Hal's concentration was still impaired by cramp and he entered the portrait in the Water Colour Society's landscape section, with Miss Walker superimposed on the new Tyne Bridge, leaning heavily on a lieutenant-colonel. The hanging committee disqualified him for artistic deviation compounded by embrocation.

In some dudgeon, he then sent the painting to Queen Mary, suggesting it might hang in the back bedroom at Windsor Castle, and asking after the King's nose. It was returned by a lady-in-waiting, who said that the only one who liked it was the garter king of arms, but not much.

It hung in our own back bedroom until Uncle Hal took up darts. Like the Royal Family, Miss Walker never cared for it, even though Uncle Hal assured her that that was how he, the artist, was permitted to see her. To be fair, nobody else saw her as a nude octahedron whose modesty was not protected by her ginger beard.

And he was sublimating his guilt over the cross-country, she asserted, when he offered to serve in the butcher's shop while Jas Hunkers was laid up with his broken big toe.

It was there that he lost his virility symbol. Not that he came to terms with his Id, although the circumstances were certainly painful, as any man who has had his moustache caught in a mincing machine will know.

A Poultice for a Poet

Last night, I thought of Herbert Mangle's aphorism, 'When life copies art, we talk at cross purposes.' He was writing his epic poem, *Desideratum*, when he came out with it, having paused between verses to rub his leg.

'I've got this aphorism,' he said to his sister.

'Would you like a poultice?' she inquired. She didn't care for *Desideratum*, or for his aphorism, but she made poultices for the cycling club and always had a spare one in her reticule.

Mangle shrugged off his troubled leg and went back to his thirteenth verse and the aphorism lay unheeded until his death, when his sister found it in an old hat.

'Mangle's *Quatrain to Mildred Grant at her Bath* is unforgettable,' my Uncle Hal once remarked to Jas Hunkers, the right-wing Wallsend family butcher.

'It was Olivia Harris,' Hunkers responded.

'Was it?' said Uncle Hal. 'How did it go again?'

How the first verse of *Desideratum* went was:

Suppose my typewriter decided to write
An ode or a sonnet instead of me,
It probably could and it very well might
Make much better use of the '2/3' key.

Mangle was a sensitive man with one ear shorter than the other, and he made a striking figure as he rode about Wallsend on his sister's bicycle with his much-patched knickerbockers and dilated nose. He had his differences with Jas Hunkers, himself an inferior poetaster:

Try our sausage; it's unique.
Our Christmas Club's two pence per week.

This misunderstanding was not unconnected with Mangle's love for the butcher's daughter, to whom he dedicated his *To My Lady's Knees*, which he laughingly claimed he would much rather rub than his own leg.

He had never intended to be a poet. He had begun as a coalman in Backworth, but was allergic to his horse, which brought him out in a purple rash.

'I feel there should be something else for me,' he said one morning to his sister over breakfast.

'I could give you devilled kidneys,' she offered.

'Pardon?' he said.

'It's just that you've always had grilled gammon,' she complained.

He stared at his plate. 'It won't do,' he said.

She delved in her reticule for a poultice.

'That's no good for a purple rash,' he said.

'I was thinking of your dilated nose,' she said.

'I'm perfectly happy with grilled gammon,' he said.

'I wish you'd make up your mind,' she muttered.

On a visit to London for the Coal-Calling

THE
COLLECTED
WORKS
OF
WORDSWORTH

Championships, he was in the National Gallery one day, sheltering from the sun, when he stepped back from *And When Did You Last See Your Father*? and fell over Augustus John, who was painting in an alcove.

'How I wish,' Mangle remarked, 'that I could carry away that wonderful colour.'

'No reason why not,' said John. 'You're sitting on my brush.'

'I'll say this,' said Mangle. 'You're making a good job of this alcove.' He came eighty-fourth in the coal-calling, but his purple rash drew a round of applause.

'I'm going to take up poetry,' he told his sister when he got back home, 'like this fellow John.'

'Close your nose,' she said, 'when you're eating your breakfast.'

'He's very nice when you get to know him,' he said. 'He lent me his hat.'

'John who?' she demanded.

'The sun was in my eyes,' he explained. 'Did I say poetry? I meant painting.'

'I got those kidneys you were on about,' his sister said.

He abandoned his horse and his coal-calling and painted for twenty-one years, but although he pleased his friends, because he had had a very loud voice, critical success eluded him. 'Who is this fool with a short ear and much-patched knickerbockers?' reviewers asked.

He had spent a great deal of that time on a painting called *And When Did You Last See Jas Hunkers, Family Butcher*?

'It may seem a bit derivative,' he said anxiously to his sister.

'Well, the sun was in your eyes,' she said, not unkindly, and offered him her bicycle for every second Tuesday, the day she stayed at home, polishing her reticule.

She and her bicycle were growing old together and she

hardly noticed when he abruptly abandoned his canvas. 'Jas Hunkers has gone to Leeds,' he explained. 'Anyway, I meant poetry after all, and besides, when life copies art, we talk at cross purposes.'

'Are you sitting on my poultice?' she asked. With advancing age, she was beginning to mislay her poultices.

'You'll notice I'm taking up aphorisms,' he said. 'That was one just now.'

But she was not herself, having had to resign from the cycling club after poulticing the club captain on the wrong leg. 'I was only one out,' she sad sourly.

Mangle was soon contributing to the *Wallsend Weekly Buffoon* his 'Random Aphorisms Composed by a Dilettante Vegetarian Cyclist In and Around the Purlieus of Wallsend,' for which he was paid by the word. This time, there was acknowledgement of sorts. 'Who is that fool with the short ear, the dilated nose and devilled kidneys on his knickerbockers?' asked Myrna Bambridge, the cookery correspondent. But he remained unaffected, except that he renovated the bicycle; there was not much he could do about his sister.

His rondeau *To My Lady's Knees*, beginning 'O gorgeous joints . . . ' caused a furore in the butcher's shop, for Mangle was making simultaneous advances to the greengrocer's niece and the two ginger barmaids at the Dun Cow. 'I love them all in different ways,' he protested. Jas Hunkers, back from Leeds, said that as far as he knew there was only one way, but he had led a sheltered life, for a butcher.

Mangle lived to be eighty-two, at which age he wrote his chef d'oeuvre, 'Rhapsody to My Sister's Bicycle', in spite of leaving his rhyming dictionary in Mildred Grant's bath:

O bike! – had I but golden tongue to name
The myriad glories of thy gorgeous frame:

Thy pump, thy handlebars, thy spokes, thy seat,
Thy tyres with balmy Wallsend wind replete.

He proved allergic to the bicycle and in 1965 died of a purple rash, leaving £73 to his sister for kidneys.

'There's this hat as well,' she told the executor, 'with an aphorism in it. It belongs to John.'

'John who?' asked the executor.

'I'm not going into all that again,' she said.

Love in a Windy Place

Ben Tapken was a blunderer. He got his head jammed behind the sideboard. He couldn't remember the formula for the area of a circle. He mislaid the hearthrug. By the age of thirty-nine, racked by fear of walking into people, he had accustomed himself to staying in behind closed curtains, venturing out only to air his prize-winning spaniel. He spent much of his time in the pantry of his sequestered home, polishing the spaniel's trophies and composing a despairing rondeau to Mrs Jane Starling, the women's bowls champion of Wallsend.

He had loved Mrs Starling with an unspoken love ever since he had first seen her in the park with the sunlight glinting on her apricot slacks. Indeed, that same night, he had emerged from the pantry and declaimed a stanza to the spaniel:

'Let me potter by the bandstand,
Like the mooniest of fools,
At the sylvan scene on the velvet green
Where Jane is pitching bowls.'

The spaniel had stared back at him with wonder in her sad gaze. Her gaze was sad because she had always wanted to be a police dog, but the police rejected spaniels on the grounds that their ears got in their eyes.

Months went by and Tapken lay on the hearthrug, when he could find it, forcing himself to acknowledge that he must overcome his blighting ineptitude. 'Otherwise, how shall I ever declare my love?' he asked the spaniel. The spaniel didn't answer. Apart from her own sense of rejection, she was still wondering at his effrontery in rhyming 'bowls' with 'fools'.

Douglas Naylor did not love Mrs Jane Starling, or any other lady, which might have been because he was secretary of the Bowls Club, and human proximity diminishes a divinity, as Erasmus said, in Dutch. More probably it was because he was a misogynist. The trouble with women, he claimed, was that they kept flicking dust off you, or straightening your pullover, or wanting to push your ears forwards and sideways.

He had once been in love, with a pert-nosed girl, and had had every intention of marrying her as soon as Blyth Spartans won the European Cup. One night, however, as they sat under the soft lights of a cafeteria, and he was telling her of his hopes and aspirations, he realised that she was staring at him, not in rapt interest in his words, but because there was a bit of sausage on his tie. He broke off the engagement, moved house and joined the Bowls Club by way of anti-compensation, because he hated bowls, and settled down thereafter to a bachelor's existence, hugging his grudge, going home nightly from the bowling green to sit at his antiquated television set, and boiling his own potatoes and washing his own socks. He now loved only Blyth Spartans, but gave them up to fuel his asperity, and took up pipe-smoking, which he loathed.

There came a day when a cat walked into his life with a sprained ankle sustained in a quarrel with a sparrow. Something told Douglas Naylor that human proximity would not diminish a cat, so he nursed him back to strength and named him Tommy after his late aunt. As he slumped of a night with his back to his television set, for he was a compulsive non-viewer, he would tell the cat of his hopes and aspirations. The cat would only say, 'Miaow.'

Meanwhile, Ben Tapken for his part was seeking to fight his way out of bachelordom. Having taken a correspondence course in bowls, he steeled himself to visit the park and join the club, leaving the spaniel with his neighbour, Miriam Burns, a lady with a nostalgic air, who had moved to the area after sundry mortifications, which she had tried to tell him about over the fence, but he had pleaded fear of walking into her.

'I've known love,' she told him.

'I'm growing this beard,' he said. His deflective conversation had rebuffed several previous neighbours.

He went to the Bowls Club, disguised, and wearing his newly-grown beard to mask his bashfulness, but the plan misfired because he was greeted by Douglas Naylor, who mistook him for King George the Fifth and invited him to become president.

'What?' said Tapken, who was adjusting his false nose and failed to hear.

'Will twenty guineas be all right, sire?' Naylor suggested.

'Have you a Mrs Starling?' asked Tapken.

'Pardon, sire?' said Naylor.

'I've got this rondeau, you see,' said Tapken, shifting his wig and knocking out Naylor's pipe with his elbow.

'I knew he wasn't King George the Fifth,' Naylor told the

club captain afterwards, 'when his nose fell off.'

The captain, a resigned man, given to saying, 'Oh, well,' intimated that a certain singularity was acceptable in a president. But something bothered him about Naylor's story. 'This is 1984, you know,' he said.

'There is that,' Naylor admitted. 'By the way, he has a rondeau,' he warned.

'It's a windy place,' said the club captain, who was thinking of a 'bandeau'.

Naylor went home to mend the leg of his television set. It was then that he decided to teach the cat to sing, arguing that if he was a happy cat he might learn to go out and fetch in the provisions of potatoes and socks. 'This will leave me more time,' Naylor reasoned, 'to hug my grudge.' For three months, the cat pretended to try very hard to sing, but his encounter with the sparrow had left him neurotic, and he had developed a self-induced deafness.

'Speaking of my late aunt,' Naylor said one night, 'as we were three months ago, you might think, puss, that Tommy was a funny name for her.'

The cat said, 'Miaow.'

'I can explain,' said Naylor.

'Miaow,' said the cat.

'Never mind,' said Naylor.

An hour later, as they sat by the television set, not watching BBC2, the cat suddenly began to sing the Introduction to the Third Act of *Lohengrin*. Naylor had lapsed deeply into misogyny and heard nothing, but the sound of Wagner caused the leg to come off the television set again, and the whole thing crashed on to his foot, occasioning painful, albeit minor, injuries. 'For three months he teaches me music,' the cat sighed, 'and the first time I sing something, he dislocates his toe.'

Naylor had seized the telephone and was dialling 999.

'Have you an ambulance for my foot?' he moaned.

'You'll have to speak up,' a female voice replied. 'There's some Wagner on the line.'

'I think it's the metatarsal,' said Naylor.

'I can't hear you,' shouted the voice.

'I can't hear you,' shouted Naylor.

'I think it's the *Meistersinger*,' said the voice.

'I'll have to ring off,' shouted Naylor. 'The socks are boiling.'

He went to bed with only his grudge for comfort.

The cat sang a bit of *Parsifal* outside the bedroom door, but was beginning to wonder if he should move on. He had considered the comforts of the Fire Station before plumping for life with Naylor; his mother had once been rescued from a tree by a fireman. The fact that she had been quite happy up the tree didn't vitiate the altruism. All firemen mean well; that's their tragedy.

'Oh, we get some peculiar calls,' Miriam Burns said to Tapken the next evening.

'I was hoping you would look after the spaniel,' Tapken said. 'You do like butterscotch, don't you?'

'I'm a telephone operator, you see,' Miriam Burns divulged. 'It's one of the mortifications I was wanting to tell you about.'

'I'm off to the Bowls Club, then,' Tapken said, avoiding the sideboard. 'They've made me president. Have you seen my nose?'

Miriam Burns and the spaniel settled down with the butterscotch, both thinking there must be greater things in life.

As it happened, Tapken had made only one sortie on to the bowling green that summer, cracking the club captain's ribs when a bowl slipped out of his hand. He had spent the

rest of the season sitting miserably among the overshoes in the changing closet, listening to Mrs Starling's tinkling voice in the ladies' room next door and composing a sonnet to her apricot slacks. Was this worth twenty guinaes, he asked himself? He finished the sonnet one September evening and slipped wearily out into the chrysathemum-laden dusk for a breath of air and to shift his wig. Had he but known, his singularity had not gone unnoticed by the statuesque widow. 'Who is that droll person breathing on the chrysanthemums?' she asked Naylor.

'Well, he's not the king,' said Naylor sourly. 'He knocked my pipe out.'

'It doesn't follow,' said Mrs Starling.

'I shouldn't be here,' Naylor said, rubbing his foot.

'Why does he sit among the overshoes?' Mrs Starling enquired.

'As a matter of fact, he's the president,' Naylor vouchsafed.

'I suppose it's the next best thing,' said Mrs Starling.

Summer gave way to autumn, as it does in Wallsend, and there had loomed up the Bowls Club Annual Dance and Prizegiving, an auspicious event, although depleted in advance by virtue of Naylor's toe and the club captain's ribs. Tapken ironed his trousers that night and sponged 'Stuffo' tinned dog–food from his dinner jacket, the while concocting a last amorous plan. He had resolved that when the time came for him to present Mrs Starling with the President's Cup for the Ladies' Championship, the moment would be equally opportune to press his rondeau, or his sonnet, on her.

He set out for the dance, bearing cup, sonnet and rondeau, dizzy with hope. 'After all,' he told the spaniel, 'I've remembered πr^2. Anything is possible.'

The spaniel declined to reply, this time because she had

a lonely night in prospect. 'I have to visit a sick misogynist,' Miriam Burns had explained. 'Did I mention that I'm a member of a voluntary orgaisation for visiting sick misogynists?'

'Have you had any mortifications lately?' Tapken asked politely, but only because he had forgotten the butterscotch.

Miriam Burns went off to visit the anonymous mysognynist. She found him nursing his toe in front of a three-legged television set, wearing a twisted pullover and covered in dust. They had a tearful reunion, he knocked out his pipe and they recalled her pert nose and the sausage on his tie and they laughed a little over it all. She left at midnight, telling him she didn't love him. There was a cat singing in the background.

Tapken's spaniel was not singing. Forsaken in the sequestered home, she at first sublimated by chewing some old sonnets. Then, leaping on to the kitchen bench to demolish the closed curtains, she discovered that the window was open. She jumped out into the night. She was going for greater things.

Tapken had sat quaking in the cloakroom until the hour for the presentations arrived. Then they fetched him out and pointed him at the platform. A propitious moment for conveying to Mrs Starling his rondeau or sonnet never materialised, for he had to present her first with the cup, and he had brought the wrong one from his pantry, so that the trophy she found thrust into her arms was inscribed: 'For the bitch of the year'.

'Mind you, captain,' he said next day, 'there was no need for her to punch my false nose.'

'Your elbow,' the captain said.

'Still,' said Tapken, 'I daresay I can write a palinode about it.'

'It's in my eye,' said the club captain.

In any case, Mrs Starling had decided that she loved Douglas Naylor, the dusty misogynist. 'He has such human proximity,' she reasoned. Six weeks later, she married him. He wore a newly-straightened pullover, adjusted his ears and abandoned his hopes and aspirations, which, as the cat mused, is the best thing for a man to do when he gets married or supports Blyth Spartans.

That was the cat's last word. He resumed his neurotic limp and went off, hoping to join the Fire Brigade or climb a tree and be happy, but he met a dog with her ears in her eyes who was running away from boredom and 'Stuffo' tinned dog–food, and together they founded the Northumbrian Cat and Dog Misanthropic Society. As Erasmus said, in Dutch, God is frequently mocked.

The reason why Ben Tapken's neighbour, Miriam Burns, was unable to love Naylor was that, unrebuffed, she had come to love Ben Tapken. So it was a double wedding in Wallsend. Both brides were given away willingly by the Bowls Club captain, who wished them all every happiness in their future life in Australia.

'We're not going to Australia,' said Tapken.

'Oh, well,' said the club captain.

Ambition's Debt

Uncle Hal used to hanker for a sundial, but there was one of those domestic compromises and my old Aunt Emma got a black-and-white cat.

We had a grandfather clock which stood outside the gas meter cupboard and Uncle Hal stared at it uncomprehendingly every morning before checking the draught in the scullery with his wet finger and going across the backlane to manure his allotment.

'I could tell the time by the stars,' he told my old Aunt Emma, 'but you can't really manure your allotment by starlight.'

My old Aunt Emma said the clock would be perfectly all right if it had a minute hand. 'You could ask Jas Hunkers,' she said. 'I wish you'd wipe your boots.'

Jas Hunkers, Family Butcher, the first Do It Yourself man in Wallsend, had a supply of minute hands, but he kept them for customers who bought his best mince.

'You're sitting on *Julius Caesar*,' said Uncle Hal.

'I don't know where all the manure comes from,' said

my old Aunt Emma.

Uncle Hal retrieved the warm copy of *Julius Caesar* and told me to hurry with it to my English master. It was the bright day that brought forth the adder, he said, and he was going back to his allotment to find a site for a sundial.

My English master was a tenacious man who nagged me to prune my adverbs, but Uncle Hal doubted whether academics prepared a lad for the real world in which clocks had to be altered twice a year. There was admittedly a mention of clocks striking in *Julius Caesar*, but this was an anachronism, according to the English master.

I thought him infallible at the time, but I learned later that he always mispronounced 'onomatopoeia', although even to get close taxed his tenacity.

For the Speech Day production of *Julius Caesar*, he cast me as Cinna, who was torn for his bad verses, but I left my bald wig in the Fourth Form classroom (girls'), because I was worried at the time about the North Pole, which had come up in a science lesson about longitudinal differentials.

Uncle Hal said this was a manifestation of the class structure in geography; it was enough to make him believe in the flat earth theory, except that he already did. As it was, I was handicapped by playing Cinna without my glasses, which would have been another anachronism, the English master suspected. After all, Caesar, who was deaf, he said, didn't have an ear trumpet.

It was rather much to expect that Herbert Mangle, the Wallsend poet, would stand back from controversy, and a verse entitled *Certitude* appeared in the *Wallsend Weekly Buffoon*:

Galileo perfected the pendulum clock,
After which he re-fashioned the pulley and block.
He refined hydrostatics and then, very soon,

He deduced the existence of Jupiter's moon.
But a moment arrived when his dreams seemed
undone,
For he swore that the earth made a path round the
sun.
So they put him in prison. But still, to his shame,
He emerged with a highly preposterous claim:
'I shall move the whole earth, which no man can
forbid,
If you'll give me a lever.' But nobody did.

And nobody had the heart to tell Herbert Mangle that it was Archimedes.

Longitudinal differentials were explained to me by the girls' science mistress, whom I kept in with because I had trysts at the Fourth Form radiator with one of her pupils who played Calpurnia with a false chest. The science mistress supported the genetical theories of Linnaeus. She anticipated a world energy crisis and dreamed of dynasties founded on the model of the Infusorian Amoebas. As far as I know, she didn't mispronounce any of this, but I can't speak for myself.

My wig was brought into the Forum by Calpurnia, panting, and being without glasses I at once stabbed her, under the impression that she was Julius Caesar, as I explained when they prematurely lowered the curtain.

'You're a poet, not a conspirator, you fool!' shouted the English master.

'What I was thinking about, sir,' I said, 'was the North Pole, where there aren't any longitudinal differentials and so, according to my Uncle Hal, it's always any time you want it to be for manuring.'

He uttered a low moan, which I identified as

onomatopoeic, and said he would see me at Philippi, if he couldn't avoid it.

Next day, Uncle Hal bought half-a-pound of best mince and called in Jas Hunkers to the grandfather clock. 'It's well known, you see,' he told my old Aunt Emma, 'that sundials held their own against grandfather clocks until Willett's Daylight Saving Bill, 1908, when the difficulty of putting sundials forward an hour defeated the best Edwardian brains.'

'You'll get arthritis in that finger,' said my old Aunt Emma.

Jas Hunkers looked at the clock and said Uncle Hal must have noticed that the hour hand had now dropped off. 'You can't get hour hands,' he said severely. 'That clock will just whir and expire.'

'What I'd really like is a sundial,' Uncle Hal said.

'They don't work outside gas meter cupboards,' Jas Hunkers warned. 'You could try Walter Eames.'

'What about my allotment?' Uncle Hal asked.

'It certainly needs a change of manure,' Jas Hunkers acknowledged. 'But Walter Eames can't help you there. He's a monumental sculptor.'

'I always thought of him as a small man,' said Uncle Hal. 'Will he do me a sundial?'

'He does a very nice headstone,' said Jas Hunkers, 'but only for cemeteries.'

I had been hanging about, hoping to redeem myself by explaining to my old Aunt Emma where manure came from, but it seemed she already knew, so it was a dispiriting time for me. Calpurnia, once she had removed the dagger from her false chest, had put an end to our trysts, which was a disappointment to the science mistress, who had predicted that we were genetically equipped to found a dynasty of nincompoops.

Of course, there have been other radiators in my life, but I still remember Calpurnia's chest (at least) when I think of the Infusorian Amoebas, which isn't very often these days. Mind you, I've lived to prune adverbs and see *Julius Caesar* performed with an ear trumpet at the National Theatre, but I don't recall that Herbert Mangle was ever torn by readers of the *Wallsend Weekly Buffoon*.

Three weeks after the domestic compromise, the grandfather clock whirred and expired.

'Aye, well,' said Uncle Hal, 'I'm not getting a headstone.'

Public Exposures

Herbert Mangle, the neo-Wordsworthian poet, used to claim that Councillor Mrs Thelma Dutt vied with the pit heap as Wallsend's noblest landmark. He was violently in love with her for three weeks, and one night was reading to her his *Lines Written to a Vast Widow*, when she perched on his knee and displaced a cartilage, rendering him unfit to keep goal for Wallsend Amnesia football team.

My Uncle Hal, Marxist team manager, upbraided this familiar Mangle surrender to the flesh and called on the Sunday School superintendent instead for the 'derby' match against Percy Main Static. The superintendent pointed out that he had a sprained thumb, sustained in striking the lectern during a sermon entitled 'Guard Thine Honour'. Nevertheless, he acknowledged that he smelt the battle far off and was willing to say among the trumpets, Ha ha.

'That's all right, then,' said Uncle Hal.

He would have preferred to hand the goalkeeper's jersey to Seppy Elphinstook, the celibate barber, who, because of his knock knees, seldom let a ball between his legs, but Elphinstook had lapsed into one of his misogynist spells, sitting in front of his fire, with his big toe sticking out of his sock, hating women.

'Mind you,' Uncle Hal told my old Aunt Emma, 'the serious horrors are those which seem respectable to respectable men.'

'Eat your apple dumpling,' said my old Aunt Emma.

When Seppy Elphinstook had been an eager young man in Hebburn, his father had planned for him a vaulting career as a tram inspector, but he hankered after the glamour of hairdressing and ran away to Wallsend, swearing that his immortal soul was not to be compromised.

Now, with the onset of middle age, he was sunk in disillusionment. Hairdressing had turned out to be less than fulfilling, and while the shop was full of shaggy customers, he would languish in his kitchen, dashing off wild water paintings of nude historical characters, in the time he could spare from hating women.

To Herbert Mangle, hating women was an alien philosophy. As it happened, even as he suffered his dislocated cartilage, he was about to break with Mrs Dutt anyway, because he had just got engaged to the two ginger barmaids at the Dun Cow. When the rupture came, however, Mrs Dutt blamed it on Uncle Hal, her ancient adversary, and next day she cut him dead when she came on him standing on his hands down by the Gut.

There had been animosity between them since the council elections, when Uncle Hal had opposed her, standing as a Theoretical Nudist, his contention being that there was a pressing need for nakedness in politics. 'No politician,' he told my old Aunt Emma, 'could indulge in pompous dissimulation while the absurdities of his physique were plain to see.'

'The blood'll rush to your head,' said my old Aunt Emma.

Thelma Dutt was a highly moral woman, president of the League of Decent Ladies, and she frequently censured the public exposure of footballers' knees. After a bitter election campaign, she had been returned with a majority of 897; Uncle Hal's eleven votes were cast by Wallsend Amnesia first team plus one reserve, Herbert Mangle spoiling his paper by writing on the back a sonnet to the Returning Officer's wife's buttocks.

Uncle Hal, while regretting his increasing shagginess, felt a distinct sympathy for Seppy Elphinstook, not least because he was himself a theoretical bachelor with theoretical nudist undertones. Shaw, he told my old Aunt Emma, had pointed out that marriage was a monstrous impediment, although we should all remember that when the Life Force beckoned, we had to follow.

'Have you seen my pudding cloth?' asked my old Aunt Emma.

Just at that time, the Life Force had lured Uncle Hal into the Nonconformists' Philosophy and Ping Pong Group and he inaugurated his year of chairmanship by promoting an Art Exhibition, in the time he could spare from standing on his hands.

The reason why he performed daily handstands in his football pants, bringing the blood to his head, was partly that he was in training for the 'derby' match and partly that the upside-down view across to the pit heap called out his austere love of the primitive. It was this same craving for the natural life that had prompted him to take the job of temporary Turkish Baths attendant, pending the advent of a Marxist society.

Seppy Elphinstook's submission to the Art Exhibition was a wild water painting depicting Sir Walter Raleigh introducing potatoes to England in the nude. Uncle Hal applauded this. Could Asquith, he asked Mrs Dutt, have denied the vote to women if he had stood naked at the Despatch Box?

Mrs Dutt said he was incorrigible, but she might at least redeem a misguided celibate, and she sped to the barber's shop, where she found Seppy Elphinstook sobbing softly over a nude of Nelson falling at Trafalgar. It was in that moment that the Life Force beckoned to a vast widow.

Meanwhile, Herbert Mangle's engagement to the two barmaids was broken off when he absent-mindedly read to them his lines dedicated to Mrs Dutt:

If Helen's face could launch a thousand ships,
Ten thousand might be sunk by Thelma's hips.

My old Aunt Emma never found her pudding cloth, and yet she steamed an apple dumpling on the eve of the football match, which may have been why Uncle Hal's shrunken football pants on that sorry occasion revealed some of the absurdities of his physique. The Sunday School superintendent was ordered off after calling the referee a latter-day Nebuchadnezzar, and Wallsend Amnesia lost 23-0.

The following Monday, Uncle Hal, demoralised by this and by Herbert Mangle's elopment with the nurse who had set his cartilage, entered the Turkish Baths and wandered in error into the ladies' department. The only occupant was Mrs Dutt and in the horrified three-and-a-half minutes before he fled, he verified the accuracy of Herbert Mangle's lines.

Next morning, he was hand-standing by the Gut in shrunken pants when Mrs Dutt came along. He gazed fixedly at the upside-down pit heap and waited to be cut down. As it transpired, however, it was the first time in

Wallsend's history that a theoretical nudist had to guard his honour from a Decent Lady.

Not that the Life Force was to be denied. Mrs Dutt sped again to the barber's shop, and so it came that Seppy Elphinstook, joining the ranks of respectable men, painted a ruff around Raleigh's neck and succumbed, with mended sock, to matrimony. All it cost him was his immortal soul.

Third Time and Still Unlucky

A few words first about Titus Andronicus the Second and then we'll move on to Nelson Weaver. Titus Andronicus the Second was a short-sighted horse. Throughout his racing career, he had never finished better than fifteenth because the wind, he claimed, had always been in the wrong direction. He lived in resentful retirement in a field near Corbridge, convinced that, given another chance, he could run fourteenth in the Northumberland Plate.

'It was the wind, Dobbin,' he would tell his companion in the field, 'except when it was the sun.'

'Moo,' his companion would reply, because she was not, as Titus believed, a donkey, but a cow named Cynthia.

In the nearby farmhouse lived their owner, Nelson Weaver, who spent much of his time under the stairs, scratching his chest, because he was immersed in insecurity. He was a small bachelor with hair growing out of his ears. He dreamed of having a wife one day, if only to cut his right-hand finger nails, but he was frightened of women and had been ever since he had been in love with two beautiful bibliophiles named Ambrosine Lang and Georgette Hudspeth, who had broken his heart in the County Library and Trinity Church hall respectively.

He was crouching under the stairs one morning, having heard light footsteps crossing the farmyard and a sweet voice calling, 'I have come for your rent, Mr Weaver.' He scratched his chest and held his breath, but presently the footsteps entered the house and paused at the stairs, and gazing out he was confronted by the knees of his landlady, Lavinia McInroy. They were the loveliest knees he had ever seen.

A compassionate girl, Lavinia pretended not to notice his diffidence. 'Wormwood blossom is late this year,' she said conversationally. 'My grandfather used to say when wormwood blossom be late arriving, farrowing sows will ne'er be thriving. And he was known far and wide,' she added, 'as an idiot.'

Weaver emerged. Thus encouraged, he allowed his gaze to travel beyond her knees. And so it began.

It had been the same, of course, with Ambrosine Lang, whose knees he had first seen up a ladder among the philosophy shelves. He had reflected then that they were the loveliest knees he had ever seen. It was in the days when he used to spend a lot of time at the County Library, talking earnestly to the young lady assistants, sometimes about books. He was youthful then and very anxious to frequent doctor and saint and hear Great Argument, but up to that time he hadn't met any saints and when he approached the doctor with a view to Great Argument, he was given some ointment for his leg.

'I was thinking of Omar Khayam,' he said.

'This is just as good,' the doctor assured him.

'There's nothing wrong with my leg,' he pointed out.

'You're young yet,' the doctor said. Nelson Weaver came out by that same door wherein he went.

It was Ambrosine Lang who came down her ladder and introduced him to Jeremy Bentham in a quiet corner between Philosophy and Political History. 'I think you'll find that the test of an institution's utility lies in how far it tends to promote the greatest happiness,' she whispered.

'What was that?' he said.

'Jeremy Bentham said that,' she said.

'Who?' he asked.

'1748–1832,' she breathed.

'I didn't catch that about the test of utility,' he said.

'Sh!' said a man in Political History.

Of course, Nelson Weaver had learned to apprehend more of Ambrosine Lang than her knees. And now it was happening again. In the weeks that followed his emergence from the farmhouse stairs, he took in Lavinia McInroy's elbows. They too were superb. There came a day when, as she marked up his rent book and handed him one-and-sixpence change, their fingers intertwined. 'Lavinia,' he ventured, 'when crab apples dangle on the bough, the milk will flow from dried-up cow.'

'I didn't know that,' said Lavinia.

Weaver lifted his gaze to her chin. It was magnificent. 'I'm a bit of a lonely chap,' he acknowledged.

'So am I, really,' said Lavinia. 'Except, of course, that I'm a girl.'

'That's true,' said Weaver. 'I wonder . . . '

'Yes?'

'I've an awful cheek, I know, and my ears aren't up to much, but would you marry me some time and share my little home – or rather, *your* little home?'

She had not expected this, or not much. 'Let me say, Collingwood . . . ' she said.

'Nelson.'

'What?'

'I'd rather you called me Nelson.'

'All right, Collingwood. But home, you know, is the girl's prison and the woman's workhouse.' She was given to quoting Shaw as well as her grandfather. 'Not to mention,' she added, 'that marriage is an intolerable obstacle to individual evolution.'

At the sound of this bruising received wisdom, all the old insecurity rushed back and Weaver scratched his chest. She regarded this in horror. It was a side of him she had not guessed at. 'Goodbye,' she murmured. 'In any case, I am going around the world on a small patrimony.' And taking £11.13s.4d in advance, she swept out.

Months went by during which Nelson Weaver scratched his chest uncontrollably. By what right had he approached this cool goddess? A short bachelor with hairy ears and a dismayed expression (we forgot to establish his dismayed expression) could not hope to achieve his heart's desire for a beautiful wife.

And yet he had hoped to marry Ambrosine Lang when she had weaned him from Jeremy Bentham and introduced him to Hegel, with the whispered aphorism that progress resulted from the interaction of two conflicting half-truths.

'I don't understnd that,' he had said.

'Neither do I,' she admitted, 'but you must appreciate that my rôle vis-a-vis yourself is catalystic rather than didactic.'

'Pardon,' he said.

She was an ethereal girl, albeit with voluptuous hips, and he feared that she might well have been wedded to her shelves, but there came an hour in that quiet corner between Philosophy and Political History when, resolved that he must know, he begged her to marry him and explain to him Immanuel Kant's *Critique of Pure Reason*.

Ambrosine Lang gazed at him for a long moment. 'You must believe,' she said at last, 'that this has nothing to do with the tea-stains on your pullover, but the fact is I have decided to marry a gas engineer and go to Glasgow.'

'Thank God for that,' said the man in Political History.

Avoiding the hurt in Nelson's eye, Ambrosine Lang whispered 'Goodbye,' turned and went off to apply Bentham's Law to Scotland and the gas industry, leaving him with nothing but Immanuel Kant.

As he sat glumly on his homeward bus, he saw alongside him the knees of Georgette Hudspeth. On them lay the complete works of Oliver Goldsmith, and so, in the time it took for the bus to disgorge them at Trinity Church hall play-reading group, he was seduced from philosophy to drama. The many moonlit walks home that followed had little to do, he knew, with the Great Argument, but he barely resisted because she was a lovely young B.A., and he was progressing beyond her knees to her silken hair and the sweet-scented back of her neck.

There was still, be it said, a shred of philosophy left in him. 'The ultimate nature of reality remains forever inaccessible,' he told himself, but, besotted by Georgette Hudspeth, he was in no shape to fathom what Immanuel Kant meant by that, although it was fair to say that he had never fathomed Nietzsche, Descartes or Kierkegaard either. The seasons came and went. It was in the days when the seasons did that. He read plays in a mist.

Now, on the little farm, the seasons had come and gone again. Sadly, he busied himself hoeing the turnips,

although he knew full well that when wind be blowing in a rush, turnips be as soft as mush.

Out in the meadow, Titus Andronicus the Second was recalling the time he had failed to clear the first jump at Hexham Steeplechases.

'That was the grandstand, mind you,' said Cynthia the cow.

'Is that so?' said Titus. 'Do you think it's my eyes, Dobbin?'

'I'd rather you called me Cynthia,' said Cynthia.

'All right, Dobbin. I'll race you to that haystack.'

'It's a telegraph pole.'

But Titus was blinking at the sun. Cynthia sighed. She had four stomachs and no upper teeth, and it was worrying her. If she had had the company of an older cow, of course, she might have learned that all cows have four stomachs and no upper teeth, but there she was, stuck in a field with a credulous horse.

Lavinia McInroy had been some way around the world. She had seen Quito, Enugu, Voronezh, Khabarovsk, Ciudad Juares and Wollongong, and would have gone on to the Rann of Kutch if her patrimony had not collapsed. In any case, she was finding, like Sebastion Cabot before her, that too much travel brings on laryngitis. She had thought of Nelson Weaver in Enugu. She had thought of him again in Ciudad Juares, when she had seen a Mexican hoeing turnips, with hair growing out of his ears.

By the time she was homeward bound for Liverpool, she was thinking of him incessantly. Absence, she reflected, makes the heart grow fonder. That's another thing about travel – it brings on platitudes.

Her letter reached the farm as Nelson hoed his last turnip of the season. 'My dear,' she wrote, 'I have seen the Grand

Canyon and the Wall of China. I have seen the Acropolis and the Pyramids. But the simple things are best, and I am coming home to you.'

Of course, in their time, Georgette Hudspeth's knees were the most beautiful he had ever seen. And not only was the back of her neck sweet-smelling. He noticed her eyes, her lips, her brow and both of her nostrils.

A day arrived when the doctor's prognosis caught up with him and he sprained his leg during a play-reading of *Hamlet*. The lovely young B.A. rubbed it as he slumped in the washplace. 'That's better than Omar Khayam,' he acknowledged.

He had hair growing out of his ears, tea-stains on his pullover and by now a button off his vest, but he knew that he must assay the bashful virgin's sidelong looks of love; Oliver Goldsmith would have expected it. 'How sweet the back of your neck smells,' he muttered one night as they lingered after *Charley's Aunt*. And he had been meaning, he added, to comment on her nostrils.

'Your teeth,' she said. 'Did you know you've got them caught in my silken hair? Goodbye.'

'Goodbye, did you say?' he said. Oh, she had gazed past him into the future and seen what life would be like with a fool who could sprain his leg reciting 'To thine own self be true,' from a sitting position.

In the years afterwards, he resorted in sorry succession to football, lepidoptera-collecting, cookery, solo whist, part-singing and on and on to turnip farming.

Well, home to the turnip farm was coming Lavinia McInroy. 'Home to you, my dear,' she wrote. 'As for your chest, I shall overlook it, or at least look the other way. Looking the other way is what makes marriage supportable. My elbows, dear, will tomorrow be yours to do with as you will, and my knees subject to further negotiation. As Shaw remarked, we have no right to consume happiness without producing it. Please telegraph that you will meet me at Corbridge station, as I have a Mexican turnip hoe.'

No sooner had Nelson Weaver read these words than he was out in the field saddling Titus Andronicus the Second. 'To the Post Office,' he cried, 'where we shall surely find happiness promoted by that institution's utility!' And he climbed into the saddle.

Instantly, Titus hurtled across the meadow, through the copse and over the turnip field, under the impression that he was running in the Northumberland Plate at last. On to the road he thundered, galloped through Corbridge, missed the bridge and plunged into the river. 'I would have won by a street,' he told Cynthia the cow afterwards, 'if the course hadn't been waterlogged.'

He recovered from his pneumonia, but only to the realisation that he would never be asked to race again. He champed moodily in his field, his heart's desire abandoned.

Nelson Weaver recovered from his pleurisy, nursed by the tender Lavinia. Her gorgeous knees became his for life; so did her hips and nostrils. And we know, don't we, that in time he found it necessary to look the other way? As Shaw remarked, one of life's tragedies is to lose your heart's desire; another is to gain it. If it comes to that, when frogs be croaking all the night, 'twill mean your crops will get the blight.

A Sanctified Artefact

The wireless would never work unless it was lying face down on its knobs in the gas meter cupboard. This suited Uncle Hal very well if he wanted to be alone with the Fat Stock Prices, but it caused certain problems when my old Aunt Emma proposed inviting the Women's Embroidery Circle in for Princess Marina's wedding.

Uncle Hal had written a letter of complaint to Stuart Hibberd, the chief announcer; he would have written to Sir John Reith himself, but as a theoretical atheist, he objected in principle to communication with that Calvinistic edifice. Stuart Hibberd replied with his best wishes and a photograph of the Boyd Neel Strings drinking cocoa in the B.B.C. canteen, but was silent on the matter of the wireless's knobs.

Uncle Hal said this offhandedness typified the decadence of the public–school classes. 'If anybody wants me,' he added, 'I'm looking at the artefact.' And he hurried down the backyard to where Silas Plews, the landlord, symbol of the discredited capitalist system, which unbelievably was still with us in A.D. 1934, had replaced the old earth closet with a flush W.C.

'History has its quirks,' Uncle Hal conceded, 'and it is a splendid artefact.'

'Waste not, want not,' said my old Aunt Emma.

'Herbert Mangle's going to dedicate it,' said Uncle Hal. 'What's "Waste not, want not" got to do with it?'

'Eat your sausage,' said my old Aunt Emma.

'That's better,' said Uncle Hal.

Herbert Mangle, the Wallsend poet, arrived next morning to sanctify the new W.C. 'After all,' Uncle Hal explained, 'bishops bless an army on the eve of a battle.'

'They seldom bless a poet,' said Herbert Mangle, 'on the eve of a sonnet.' He blew his nose and declaimed:

> 'A joy forever is a thing of beauty:
> Thus sang the poet Keats so long ago.
> Within these walls a man may do his duty
> And rise enlightened from this gorgeous po.

From that moment, Uncle Hal took to spending many an earnest hour in the W.C., compiling crossword puzzles for Hansard. When he had amassed fifteen, he posted them to Ramsay MacDonald, with the answers in invisible ink.

'I've advised him to breathe on them at the appropriate moment,' he told my old Aunt Emma, over his sausage. 'What have you done with Boyd Neel?'

'What about the wireless's knobs?' asked my old Aunt Emma.

Uncle Hal said the Boyd Neel Strings were a capitalist shibboleth and instructed that the photograph should be ceremonially thrown on the backlane Guy Fawkes bonfire, but my old Aunt Emma, noting that it was only March the tenth, murmured, 'Waste not, want not,' and volunteered to find a place to hang it.

Meanwhile, the Embroidery Circle had held an unsatisfactory trial run in the gas meter cupboard, listening to 'Keep Fit With Prunella Stack'. They were not unduly crowded, provided Granny Tate stuck one leg outside, but she felt unable to Knees Bend with only one leg available, unless she took off her farthingale, which she was not prepared to do until the clocks went forward.

The one man who might have mended the wireless was Jas Hunkers, Family Butcher, who used to charge his accumulators with bull's blood. What with this and his forty-foot aerial, he could get Tokyo. Unfortunately, this antagonised Uncle Hal, who had just proclaimed himself a Nipponophobe, denouncing Japan's emergent capitalist pretensions.

As it happened, however, it was coming up to the time of the Cup Final, so Uncle Hal swallowed his principles and wrote after all to Sir John Reith, seeking an audition for the job of shouting 'Square Four' during George Allison's running commentary. Sir John would be welcome, he said, to call at our house at any time for a cup of cocoa, and if he brought his tools they might mend the wireless between them. In return, Uncle Hal could make available his spare cap, since he had noticed from newspaper pictures that Sir John's black homburg was a bit on the shabby side.

There was no response from Sir John, so after a fortnight Uncle Hal wrote again, mentioning that as a lad at school he had been second-top in elocution. The cap was $6\frac{7}{8}$, he said. When there was still no reply after another three weeks, he closed the correspondence with a short note saying the B.B.C. was obviously a bastion of privilege; the offer of the cap was withdrawn and he would gladly see Sir John standing bald-headed in everlasting Caledonian drizzle.

It was a week later that Ramsay MacDonald travelled to Canada with Uncle Hal's parcel in his haversack in mistake for the Ottawa Agreement and left it in a barber's shop after having his moustache curled. So it came that Stanley Baldwin received a postcard saying: 'Weather showery. Please send more crosswords. As it leaves me. R. Mac.D.'

Nor was that the last blow to capitalist pretensions. Uncle Hal had prised the back off the wireless one day and scattered all the pieces on the floor when Jas Hunkers arrived, extending the hand of friendship and bringing my old Aunt Emma some black pudding. He was only a theoretical Nipponophile, it seemed, and in any case, it wasn't Tokyo he was getting but the Welsh Regional programme. He mended the set and screwed the back on and it gave no more trouble, although it was a few days before we realised what had happened to the black pudding.

The Embroidery Circle heard the royal wedding in the front room in regal comfort, with Granny Tate's right leg on the fender end and her farthingale removed only for the National Anthem.

As a theoretical republican, Uncle Hal spent the afternoon quietly with his artefact. It was here, an hour later, that my old Aunt Emma burst in on him to say that there was a tall distinguished man in a black homburg at the front door.

'Well, don't keep him standing, woman!' Uncle Hal shouted. 'Make some cocoa!' And he rushed through the house to meet Sir John, flourishing his spare cap and calling, 'Square Four!'

The man at the front door was not prepared to part with

his homburg; it was his insignia as an official of the Newcastle and Gateshead Water Company. He was empowered, he said, to go down our backyard to examine the W.C. cistern. Afterwards, Uncle Hal, murmuring 'Waste not, want not', offered him the cocoa.

'Mind you,' the man said, 'that's a funny place to hang a photograph of the Boyd Neel Strings,' so on balance it was as well he wasn't the Director General of the B.B.C.. But history has its quirks and Ramsay MacDonald spent many an earnest hour in Downing Street, breathing on the Ottawa Agreement.

Last Night, Ah Yesternight

It was on his sixty-ninth birthday that Dr Duncan resolved to learn the banjo. He had always wanted children, or a Persian cat, but his wife had run away to Spennymoor thirty-five years earlier with a wandering insurance man, leaving a rice pudding in the oven. From that first unhappy moment, he had cut a forlorn figure, sitting day after day in his dim surgery, with his pullover on backwards.

One night, as midnight boomed, he received an urgent call to go to Mrs Proudfoot at the off-licence. It was a hazardous journey, because the lamp kept going out on his bicycle and he had a slow puncture, but he was not a man to forget his Hippocratic Oath; it went everywhere with him, in his saddlebag.

The distraught widow greeted him with tears coursing down her bodice. 'It's Jumbo, my Persian cat,' she sobbed. 'He's slumped across the hearthrug, breathing thickly.'

Dr Duncan tapped the cat's knees and said it was a clear case of mumps; he would pedal back to his surgery for his forceps if she would run on in front, waving something white. She instantly doffed her camisole, saying she would do what she must. As it happened, it was a pink camisole, but all camisoles are grey in the dark, as any Persian cat lover would know.

It was the start of a sad sweet affair. Mrs Proudfoot trimmed the wick of his bicycle lamp, although the forceps were never the same again, and Dr Duncan reversed his pullover and took to playing the Peer Gynt Suites to her on his banjo, by ear. The cat, breathing thickly or not, left the hearthrug and went out for several long walks around the fish factory.

It was the view of Seppy Elphinstook, the misogynist barber, that Mrs Proudfoot would have doffed her camisole anyway. She had a history of doffing her camisole, he claimed. Herbert Mangle, the Wallsend poet, who was in love with Mrs Proudfoot just then, said this was a deplorable impugnment of the widow's honour, even though true. He was on the rebound from enormous Councillor Mrs Dutt, who was on the rebound from Seppy Elphinstook, who was on the rebound from Emily Hunkers, the butcher's daughter.

'If you've loved so many women,' said Herbert Mangle, 'how can you be a misogynist?'

'That's how,' said Seppy Elphinstook.

Herbert Mangle withdrew and composed his *Ode to Dissimulation*:

> I've loved a lot and loved too well
>   And sighed my share of sighs;
> But when I kiss I always tell,
>   Which saves a lot of lies.
> Romantic love is just a myth,
>   I've known from early youth:
> The ladies whom I've dallied with

Have taught me that bald truth.
Oh yes, I own to clay-like feet,
But then I've always found
It's sentimental self-deceit
That makes the world go round.

He then decided to elope with Mrs Proudfoot at three o'clock the next afternoon on the greengrocer's horse; he would have done it at the more quixotic hour of two in the morning, but the horse was twenty-nine and saw very badly in the dark, with or without a trimmed wick.

He placed a kitchen chair against the widow's bungalow window and gallantly climbed up it, defying his vertigo, while the horse nibbled her hollyhocks.

'Yoo-hoo, Mrs Proudfoot!' he called.

'Who's there?' Mrs Proudfoot called back.

'I've come to elope with you,' Herbert Mangle informed her.

'I'm flattered,' Mrs Proudfoot responded. 'Believe me, Mr Elphinstook, I'm flattered.'

'It's not Mr Elphinstook,' said Herbert Mangle. 'It's Herbert Mangle.'

'Whoever it is, I'm flattered,' said Mrs Proudfoot. 'But I rather think another loves me, if you can leave it for the time being.'

'Oh, well, goodbye,' said Herbert Mangle, not, be it said, unrelieved.

He climbed back into the saddle and the horse galloped into the hollyhocks, because it saw none too well in daylight.

But did another indeed love Mrs Proudfoot? Peer Gynt Suites notwithstanding, Dr Duncan lived with the memory that his wife still sent him a tie on her birthday, because she could never remember his. It was always the wrong size

and now he was just a rueful old man with a house full of ties and banjo strings. His housekeeper did her best, diligently polishing brasses, but she was no substitute for a Persian cat.

Another midnight was booming when he received a desperate message that Jumbo had been seized with a further racking spasm of mumps. It was a sentimental self-deceiving widow's ruse. He arrived to find Jumbo departing briskly for the fish factory. Mrs Proudfoot had set her table with flickering candles and tossed him a salad. Even as she expectantly watched him doff his bicycle clips, however, she sensed that their brief hour of magic had departed. His eye had resumed it forlornness and his pullover was on backwards again.

She held out the tossed salad, but they both knew that between them and the tossed salad and the forceps and the tears on her bodice there had fallen a thirty-five-year-old shadow. Nevertheless, she summoned a wistful smile as she murmured, 'At least come back if you have another slow puncture.' It would never happen. He kissed her hand and left. It was a case, said Herbert Mangle, of 'Thy breath was shed upon my soul betwixt the kisses and the wine.'

Rumour had it that the doctor's wife's paramour had long since been promoted to insurance inspector and there were tales of how the guilty couple led a wild life in Spennymoor, going to dinner dances two and three times a year. On her sixty-seventh birthday, she sent him a sock instead of a tie. She realised, she wrote, that the bird of Time was on the wing and she hoped to finish the second sock by Christmas. Dr Duncan laid the sock beside the rice pudding and sat for a long time, gazing unseeingly into the oven. He offered to play the Siegfried Idyll on his banjo to his housekeeper, but she said if it was all the same to him she had some brasses to polish.

He still had his Hippocratic Oath, of course, and made a brave stab at Herbert Mangle's vertigo, but vertigo wasn't mumps, whichever way you looked at it.

'His life was a sad anti-climax,' said Herbert Mangle, 'from the day of his wife's departure.'

'One thing would have made it a sadder anti-climax,' said Seppy Elphinstook.

'What's that?' asked Herbert Mangle.

'If she'd come back,' said Seppy Elphinstook.

Certain Vicissitudes

In Whitley Bay, there was once an eccentric Trinity House brother. On his day off from St Mary's lighthouse, he was in the habit of visiting the Marine Museum to sing sea songs to his friend the curator, followed by muffins. The curator, who was colour-blind, would say, 'All cats are grey to a colour-blind horse.' The eccentric brother would ask, 'What's that got to do with it?' not realising that the curator was resorting to hybrid apothegms to disguise the fact that he didn't like being sung to.

'You'll have to tell him some day,' his wife would say, but the curator hesitated to rebuff a man in a peaked cap.

Death intervened one afternoon, however, halfway through the third verse of *Tom Bowling, the Darling of our Crew*, and afterwards the curator remarked, 'Ah, well, he's gone on the viewless wings of poesy to Arthur's bosom.'

'Don't try your hybrids on me,' his wife rejoined. 'Another thing, you're sitting on my wireless.' She was trying to catch some esoterica on Radio 3, not an easy exercise with sea songs and apothegms all round.

There was life outside the Marine Museum, including E.S. Appleyard on his bicycle. Appleyard was a frustrated dramatist. He was a good-natured man with well-assembled elbows, but his tragedy was that he wrote plays that had been written before.

It was after the failure of his masterpiece, *Lance-Corporal Barbara*, that he sadly forsook drama and resorted instead to riding a bicycle through Whitley Bay. This was a dispiriting transmutation, as the only aesthetic satisfaction it left him was the contemplation of his well-assembled elbows, and even this vanity cost him dear. Polishing his glasses one day as he was pedalling along, so that he might see his elbows the more clearly, he crashed thunderously into St Mary's lighthouse.

When he came round, a lovely girl in a peaked cap was bending over him, applying sticking plaster to his glasses.

'Who am I?' he moaned. 'How is my bicycle? What time is it in Alberta?'

'Hush!' I am the lighthouse-keeper,' the girl murmured. 'Totter over my threshold and sample my Yorkshire pudding.' And taking his elbow, she helped him inside, where she told him, over her Yorkshire pudding, of how she had been left the lighthouse in the will of an eccentric Trinity House brother, after transcribing the third verse of *Tom Bowling* for him, unsuccessfully.

'For my part,' Appleyard volunteered, 'I have these well-assembled elbows, in case you missed the exposition, but am a good-natured man.'

'I've heard of you,' the girl responded. 'You were written by Oliver Goldsmith.'

'Merciful heaven!' said Appleyard. 'You're invading my tragedy!'

'There, there!' the girl said, which he was in no shape to deny.

For our first allusive glimpse of the eccentric Trinity House brother's great-great-grandmother, we must go back to 1874 and *Ursula's Horn-Rimmed Glasses*. This was an unknown opera by unknown composer, Vladek Hojid, which leaves little to be said about it, except by a diligent liar.

It was the only opera finished by Hojid, because his wife kept mislaying the piano in the course of moving house.

'I don't understand why we have to move house so much,' he protested one day when he was thirty-one.

'Have you seen the colander?' she asked. She usually mislaid the colander as well.

He was forty-one when Smetana gave him a spare piano for his birthday with the admonition to keep one foot on it whenever his wife showed signs of removing. 'I don't know what you want with two pianos,' his wife said. 'What we need is a spare colander to drain this cabbage.'

She had an addiction to draining cabbage, her mother having seen a Slovene, as handsome a non sequitur as we're likely to come across.

In any case, Hojid's musical verve was beginning to wane by then, owing to political pressure. He had just been elected to the Chamber of Deputies as an anarchist, on a programme of abolishing the Chamber of Deputies, to which he never went on principle.

'I wish you'd finish *Ursula's Horn-Rimmed Glasses,*' Smetana said to him one morning.

'Finish what?' said Hojid, because he hadn't started it.

'I must be thinking of *Die Fledermaus,*' said Smetana.

'I thought *you* wrote that,' said Hojid.

'I will, Oscar, I will,' said Smetana.

'My name's Vladek,' said Hojid.

'If it comes to that, *you're* thinking of Strauss,' said Smetana.

'Anyway, I have to go and get a colander,' said Hojid. 'We've just moved house again.'

It was as a result of this conversation that Hojid sent in his resignation to the Chamber of Deputies. 'Who?' said the Speaker.

Bedevilled as he was by anarchism and cabbage, it came as a shattering coup de grace to Hojid when his wife moved house again, mislaying both pianos and his metronome. In the event, she was only one jump ahead of the ruling Moravian Repressive Party, who came for him that night, and he spent the next three years under forced labour in the Wenceslas Christmas cracker factory. How the opera came to be finished is also unknown.

E.S. Appleyard's history is less obscure. Shortly after his contretemps alongside St Mary's, he married the loveliest lighthouse-keeper in Whitley Bay, and they settled down in the lighthouse with the bicycle and a Labrador dog that had been left in the Trinity House brother's codicil. Appleyard had never intended to get married, but had formed an addiction to Yorkshire pudding no less than Mrs Hojid's to draining cabbage. Thus does life entrap the artist.

Meanwhile, in the Marine Museum, the curator had taken to re-transcribing the third verse of *Tom Bowling* for the sake of his departed friend and was singing it daily to the fish.

'The thing is,' he said to his wife, 'if music be the food of love, unarm, Eros!'

'What with you singing sea songs,' his wife complained, 'I've missed some more esoterica.' She had followed Radio 3 since its inception and had in consequence become an authority in Whitley Bay on unknown works of art, whenever she could get away from muffins.

In the lighthouse, the months went by. Day after day, Appleyard learnt over the rail, salt spray on his glasses, growing fat, when all the while he might have been writing *Richard the Fourth* or *The Agitated Duck*. Life was comfortable and yet something constantly gnawed away inside him, apart from Yorkshire pudding. The dog lay at his heels, also bathed in dejection, pining for his old master's sea songs.

'Have I betrayed my destiny?' Appleyard asked himself. 'Is my muse in perpetual slumber? What time *is* it in Alberta?'

In Whitley Bay, it was Christmas time. Dinner was over in the lighthouse. The surf boomed and gulls ululated in a sullen sky, inserting the mandatory onomatopoeia. 'And now for the crackers!' cried Appleyard's lovely wife, as she joyfully dispensed rhubarb wine.

When Vladek Hojid, back in 1877, smuggled a dozen crackers out of the Wenceslas cracker factory, his wife took them, concealed in her stocking tops, to the Speaker of the Chamber of Deputies, to implore clemency.

'It there no justice in this land?' she demanded.

'I don't know about that,' said the Speaker. 'I've been laid up with my breathing.'

As luck would have it, the Speaker was unseated the very next week, when the Moravian Repressives were ousted by the Feudal Oligarchists. Forced to flee the country, he prevailed on Mrs Hojid to accompany him. 'Our shared love of cabbage-draining has captivated me,' he explained.

'I though it was my stocking tops,' she said demurely.

After certain vicissitudes, they settled in North East England, for the sake of his breathing, and there they founded a colander industry, for which they were granted a charter by the burgesses.

'It'll keep your stocking tops up,' said the Speaker. He

thought the burgesses had said 'garter'.

The Feudal Oligarchists were swiftly overturned by the Agrarian Separatists, and Hojid found himself released from his forced labour. 'This is on the understanding that you renounce anarchism,' the commandant told him, offering him a second-hand metronome to start a new life.

'Mind you, I renounced it before I went in,' said Hojid.

'I wish you'd said,' said the commandant.

Arriving at his back door, Hojid was met by Smetana, who said anxiously, 'Your wife has fled, Johann.'

'Thank God for that, although my name's Vladek,' said Hojid. 'Now I can marry my mistress, the Princess Caroline zu Sayn-Wittgenstein.'

'I thought that was Liszt,' said Smetana.

'We're not going into all that again,' said Hojid.

But we left Mrs Appleyard dispensing rhubarb wine.

'These crackers,' she intimated, heaping coincidence on exposition, 'were brought here in 1877, when the late Trinity House brother's great-great-grandmother arrived on these shores, seeking sanctuary from non sequiturs and worse.'

So the crackers were pulled and the mottoes read amid the usual dismal scenes of Yuletide rejoicing. Mrs Appleyard's motto read, in Slovene: 'You are lovable to a fault.' The dog's read: 'So are you.' Appleyard's read: 'Help!' I need a librettist for my opera, *Ursula's Horn-Rimmed Glasses*.'

On the instant, Appleyard's muse was re-aroused. He leapt on his bicycle and pedalled away and out of his lovely wife's life forever, with no thought even for the assemblage of his elbows. The Labrador dog was hard behind him.

Appleyard's libretto for *Ursula's Horn-Rimmed Glasses* tells the story of the land of Tantobia under threat of war and a rather severe snowstorm. Ursula, the wife of Xenophulos, the queen's chamberlain, is a bad-tempered woman with horn-rimmed glasses. Most mornings at breakfast, she kicks his leg under the table, pretending it is an accident.

Claudio, the next-door neighbour, has been condemned to die for speaking ill of the queen's basset-hound. He protests his innocence, but cannot explain away the basset-hound bites on his left calf. The cleaning lady, Yvette Lafiche, comes in and sings the aria, 'By Gum, The Bus Was Crowded This Morning'.

Xenophulos runs away to take refuge in a convent. 'You can't come in here; this is a convent,' the abbess tells him. He pleads short-sightedness, although, as we know, it is his wife who wears glasses.

The invasion force of Moors and Tartars has now been sighted and the queen puts aside her basset-hound, saying, 'We'll have to look into this.' She sends for Xenophulos, not knowing that he is in a rough alehouse, which is where he ran to after the convent.

Claudio arrives, disguised as an evil washerwoman, and says she (that is, he) will lift the curse which he (meaning she) has put on the land if the queen will pardon Claudio. 'Who's he again?' asks the queen. Claudio sings the aria, 'Did You Know There's A Smut on Your Nose?' because he no longer cares.

Act Four begins with Ursula in a bad temper again, because the snow is on her glasses and she hasn't even been out of the kitchen yet. The invasion force is drawing ever nearer and the queen is reduced to praying for wind. Claudio meets Xenophulos in the rough alehouse. 'You've got a deep voice for a washerwoman,' Xenophulos says. 'It's me, you fool,' says Claudio. They compare the bruises on their legs and decide they are one and the same person. There is a chorus of 'Ta-ra-ra-boom-di-ay', because by general consent it seems a pretty rotten idea.

The wind does not change. The invasion force lands, but having seen the queen, decides not to abduct her after all. Ursula runs after her husband, but is misdirected by the abbess and comes on Claudio, who is in any case one and the same person, so she kicks his leg with impunity.

As the cleaning lady, Yvette Lafiche, is the queen's long-lost disguised uncle, there is a total amnesty and the basset-hound is pardoned. Amid merry cries of 'See you at Easter, then,' the invasion force pushes off. Ursula finds her glasses, although most of us didn't know they were lost, and sings, rather touchingly, the aria, 'Have You Seen Mrs Wilkinson Lately?'. The opera ends.

The libretto had been written before, in 1882, by Arrigo Boito, but Appleyard had recognised that it was his destiny to write other people's plays. The artist had sprung the trap.

What of the lovely lighthouse-keeper? Forlorn amid the ululations, she wondered endlessly what time it was in Alberta. Along the road, the Labrador dog waited patiently outside the Marine Museum. If fish could be sung to, he reasoned, why not Labrador dogs?

The curator peered out. 'Is that a grey cat?' he asked his wife.

But she was listening to *Ursula's Horn-Rimmed Glasses* on Radio Three.

The Finger in the Filing Cabinet

As far as I know, the last time there was dancing in the streets of Wallsend was when the relief of Haltwhistle was announced during the Boer War. There were cries of 'Haltwhistle is relieved!' and the acting Town Clerk led off *The Grand Old Duke of York* from the steps of the Roman pump. It had to be either *The Grand Old Duke of York* or the schottische, as these were the only two dances he knew, owing to his inadequate schooling.

'Why are they shouting "Haltwhistle is relieved"? asked his partner, a widow from the Rates Department named Mrs Watkin.

'Because it has,' he replied.

'Has what?' she inquired.

'Haltwhistle,' he said. 'Baden Powell has been relieved there.'

'On my memo it says Mafeking,' said Mrs Watkins. 'Another thing - why are you dancing *The Grand Old Duke of York* when everybody else is dancing the schottische?' Her schooling had been adequate and she could recite Browning's *Pippa Passes*.

It turned out that the acting Town Clerk had mixed up the Mafeking memo with one about the annual bowls match between Wallsend and Haltwhistle, Northumberland, and had made the wrong announcement from the steps of the Roman pump in the absence of the deputy mayor, who had got his finger caught in a Town Hall filing cabinet. The mayor and the Town Clerk were in North Shields at the time, opening a rhododendron show and had missed the last tram after the mayor had gone down with a touch of bud blast. It was what might be called a chapter of accidents. It *was* called a chapter of accidents by the *Wallsend Weekly Buffoon*, in the space for late news, upside down.

This may explain why dancing in the streets has not caught on in Wallsend, which is a pity, because I have always felt that if there is anything our Northern industrial towns need it is dancing in the streets. They have got arts centres and poss tub museums, and admittedly Wallsend Amnesia Football eleven won the Aged Miners' Charity Shield in 1922 and left it in the gents' in the Dun Cow, but there has been hardly any dancing in the streets. Of course, they built the good ship *Mauretania* in Wallsend, but against that you have to set the fact that in Haltwhistle they're still waiting for the Wallsend bowls team to turn up.

The acting Town Clerk is long gone, mind you, and the Roman pump fell down during the economic crisis in 1931, but because of these ancient events there is one distinction Wallsend can claim: it added a word to the region's vocabulary. Unbridled patriotic celebration may be 'mafficking' in other parts of these islands, but in Wallsend it's 'haltwhistling'.

Times have changed. The *Mauretania* is long gone too, although faint fragments of her saga keep surfacing in reports in the *Wallsend Weekly Buffoon* about elderly women who still make clippy mats with proggers fashioned from the old ship's scrapped brass scupper gratings. And there is also the plaque above the deputy mayor's filing cabinet, commemorating his finger. Oh, times have changed, as I remarked to a man in Wallsend last Tuesday, but he didn't catch what I said and disappeared into the Poss Tub Museum, fingering his purple corduroy tie.

Mrs Watkin fell down during the heat wave of 1919, outside the Dun Cow, after seeing the bowls team off on their annual tour of Mafeking to which the transposed memo seems to have committed them. The deputy mayor never got over his resentment, especially as his injured finger prevented him from leading off the dancing with Mrs Watkin, because he had long admired her svelte hips. 'I felt a fool with a finger in that filing cabinet,' he told her afterwards.

'You'd have felt a bigger fool announcing "Haltwhistle is relieved",' she responded, adding, 'The lark's on the wing; the snail's on the thorn.' She was born before her time and would have been at home in the Arts Centre or the Earth Closet and Flat Iron Repository. She was a beautiful woman and everybody wanted to dance with her, and the bowls team frequently did, although it was seeing her home afterwards that did their game no good at all.

When the mayor and Town Clerk got back on the first tram next morning, they roused the janitor and asked if he had anything for bud blast, but he said he had used the last of his three-in-one oil on the filing cabinet.

'What's all this, then?' the mayor asked, and the whole story came out, except that they hushed up Mrs Watkin's svelte hips.

Herbert Mangle, the Wallsend poet, mentioned these matters in his jottings, in between playing goalkeeper for Wallsend Amnesia, but it's fair to admit that the editor of the *Wallsend Weekly Buffoon* dismissed him as a trumpery fabricator.

'Factually fictitious my jottings may be,' Mangle riposted, 'but they are artistically true.' The editor pretended to sneer at this palpable oxymoron, but he worked it into the next week's badminton results.

Another of Mangle's artistic truths was embodied in his lines:

> Wallsend! – of all Tyne towns thou art the best!
> From thee, the Roman Wall lurched proudly west;
> Though be it said thou pinn'dst thy latter hopes
> On Swan and Hunter and on Haggie's Ropes.

There were thirty-one more verses, but they got possed in the tub one week with his goalkeeper's jersey.

Times have changed all right, and if you are wondering what clippy mats are, or proggers, or poss tubs, why not approach the *Wallsend Weekly Buffoon*, where they won't be very pleased to hear from you?

Well, you can take all this as a plea for more dancing in the streets of Wallsend, or more earth closets. It's not a happy history, except perhaps for elderly clippy mat makers, but at least there is that plaque to the deputy mayor's mishap, or would be if it hadn't fallen down during the fuel crisis in 1947.

But spare a thought for the acting Town Clerk. He had, after all, an inadequate schooling and became a self-made acting Town Clerk by dint of stern Victorian effort, learning *The Grand Old Duke of York* by correspondence course. It couldn't happen now, is what I'm trying to suggest, but I daresay the day will come when they'll say the same about purple corduroy ties.

Her Voice Was Ever Soft

The cat's name was Rover, because Uncle Hal had always wanted a parrot, but he lost faith in her when she began to howl every time he stood me on the scullery table to impersonate Gracie Fields.

I would have preferred to spend more time with my cigarette card collection of Famous Cricketers; I needed only George Gunn for the set and that veteran Notts opener was proving dispiritingly elusive. But Uncle Hal said impersonating Miss Fields would expand my diaphragm. If I hoped to grow up to scotch the capitalist system, he said, I would need an expanded diaphragm.

As it happened, I had been auditioned as a soloist for the school concert to raise soup for orphans, but when the music master called on me, I stood on his foot and my diaphragm, remote from its protecting scullery table, refused to yield up my voice.

'What is wrong, boy?' the music master asked.

'I've left my glasses in the chemmy lab, sir,' I offered.

He sighed and awarded the solo rôle to the ginger-haired

girl who was at that time the femme fatale of the Mixed Juniors, notable for her thwarting of ardent expectations.

The music master was a sad eccentric bachelor, easily moved to tears. He frequently sobbed over his own accompaniments and had taken to heavy smoking after the music class had rather badly mauled Purcell. He hated his job and had ambitions to be a jockey and to that end had been eating dry toast for many years, but his dream began to fade when he grew to be six feet seven.

The ginger-haired girl sang *Bless This House* with heart-rending sweetness and the music master dashed away a tear with the *Racing Handicap Book* and dismissed the audition class.

The cat disappeared from the scullery one wet night when I was singing *The Biggest Aspidistra in the World*. It was another case, according to Herbert Mangle, the Wallsend poet, of the incompatibility of life and art, whichever was which.

'Mind you,' he asked Uncle Hal, 'how would you like to listen to impersonations of Gracie Fields, knowing that your owner never looks at you without seeing the dog you might have been, given that a parrot is exotic beyond his hopes?'

Uncle Hal said nature was above art in that respect. He wasn't usually optimistic, but he had been reading *King Lear*.

'Shaw said that although Shakespeare sank to blasphemous despair,' he told my old Aunt Emma, 'to the end there was mighty music in him.'

'It's raining,' said my old Aunt Emma, 'and she hasn't got her collar on.'

The cat had run away more than once, but she usually came back for Sunday dinner, because she was addicted to Yorkshire pudding. When the weekend passed and the

scullery was still cat-bereft, my old Aunt Emma said she feared pussy might be in heaven. Uncle Hal said he hoped God remembered that the secret of Yorkshire pudding was to let the mixture stand overnight. He called 'Rover! Rover!' unavailingly in the backlane, but privately suspected that the cat had set up home with the milkman.

My own dismay was partly assuaged by my burgeoning interest in the ever-expanding diaphragm of the ginger-haired girl. At the next rehearsal, I told her of my vain quest for George Gunn.

'I have a surplus of Maurice Tates, Walter Hammonds and Patsy Hendrens,' I explained. 'But George Gunn, you see, scored a hundred in his first Test.'

She said she was sorry to hear that. 'Why not come back after home time?' she whispered, between 'Bless the roof' and 'ever open to joy and love'.

'Pardon?' I said.

'You won't need your glasses,' she said.

'What's this got to do with George Gunn?' I asked.

'Very little, I hope,' she said.

'What are you doing?' the music master demanded when he surprised me climbing in a school window at twenty-past four.

'I've left my bicycle pump in the chemmy lab, sir,' I offered.

He sighed again and went home to his lodgings. He found no solace in his lonely dry toast and tear-stained *Racing Handicap Book*. At forty-two, he knew he had little hope now of becoming a stable apprentice. His landlady kept pressing him to butter his toast and use a handkerchief and he realised that he was sinking fast into orthodoxy and might even end up married.

That night in the scullery, not a little distracted, I

transposed the second verse of *Granny's Little Old Skin Rug* with the chorus of *Walter, Walter, Lead Me to the Altar*. Uncle Hal failed to notice. He was asking himself if ripeness was all. I descended from the table and went into the gas meter cupboard with my Famous Cricketers.

'I'm going to see Herbert Mangle about King Lear,' Uncle Hal told my old Aunt Emma.

'I've got a good mind to change the milkman,' said my old Aunt Emma.

It transpired that Herbert Mangle, like Dr Johnson, could hardly bring himself to read the harrowing last act of *King Lear*, which was why he had composed his *Mortifying Lines*:

> Was Shakespeare, like his tragic hero, mad?
> How many understood his *Lear*?
> Well, precious few, I dare to fear:
> And they'd have killed the author if they had.
> I should have left the volume on the shelf.
> Was all that desolation planned?
> Did even Shakespeare understand?
> If so, he surely would have killed himself.

The cat came home; she had decided that the milkman's nocturnal hours were uncongenial. Besides, she had divined that I had abandoned the scullery table and that Uncle Hal, for his part, was prepared to abandon exotic hopes and change her name to Marjorie.

Uncle Hal put aside *King Lear*. For the moment, he said, he was more in need of an ounce of civet to sweeten his imagination and he turned up at the school concert to shed a tear at the ginger-haired girl's ravishing rendition of *Bless This House*.

It was a felicitous occasion. The music master pressed his foot on the soft pedal, wincing, and the ginger-haired girl sang 'Make them pure and free from sin' to warm applause, not least from me, even though I had left my thwarted expectations in the chemmy lab.

Next day, the music master stopped me in the corridor. One of the advantages, he said, of heavy smoking was that you acquired a large number of cigarette cards. He was anxious to get hold of Patsy Hendren and could offer George Gunn, if I was interested.